THE BOOK OF RUTH

Writer - The Holy Spirit
Illustrator - Simon Amadeus Pillario
Colours - Leslie Simonin Wilmer
Ryan Esch

ILLUSTRATION AND LETTERING

Simon Amadeus Pillario

COLOURS

Ryan Esch
Leslie Simonin Wilmer

ISBN

978-0-9956035-1-6

TRANSLATION

In this limited edition copy the translation used is the World English Bible. It is an extremely reliable translation as it is based on the ASV, just like the NASB, RSV, NRSV, Amplified Version and The Living Bible.

"The World English Bible (WEB) is a Public Domain (no copyright) Modern English translation of the Holy Bible. That means that you may freely copy it in any form, including electronic and print formats. The World English Bible is based on the American Standard Version of the Holy Bible first published in 1901, the Biblia Hebraica Stutgartensa Old Testament, and the Greek Majority Text New Testament. It is in draft form, and currently being edited for accuracy and readability."

The quote at the start of the book (Acts 10:34-35) is content taken from the Holy Bible, New Living Translation, copyright © 1996, 2004, 2015 by Tyndale House Foundation. Used by permission of Tyndale House Publishers, Inc. All rights reserved.

All typefaces used within the comic are either free for commercial use or used with permission through the inplimentation of Comiclife 3.0 software.

This special edition was self published by
The Word for Word Bible Comic Company.

Printed in UK, September 2016.

INTRODUCTION

Moses frees his people from Egypt and later Joshua leads them to conquer the whole of Canaan and the surrounding regions (modern day Israel, Jordan, Palestine and parts of Syria). When Joshua dies the people of Israel fail to keep hold of these lands, begin to forsake God and enter very dark times, called the Judges period.

Under the capricious and increasingly faithless government of the Judges period, the promised land has become war-torn and desolate.

Famine and death jolt this story into motion, making a family of God's chosen people into desperate refugees. The book of Ruth is at once historical and prophetic, it tells the intertwined lives of two dauntless women and the integral parts they play within the ultimate story of the Author and perfecter of all things.

INTERPRETATION

The Word for Word Bible Comic has avoided, as far as possible, creating a new interpretation, version or re-telling of the text. Using research to ensure the narrative is represented as authentically as possible, the pictures in the comic aim to represent what the text plainly illustrates. In the case of ambiguity, a multitude of qualified and respected Bible Commentaries (including Cundall, Lange, Archer and a range of others crosrefernced with Biblehub.com) have been deferred to.

Text is clear.	=	Draw it clearly.
Text is ambiguous but the Bible clarifies it elsewhere.	=	Draw it clearly.
Text is ambiguous but good commentators agree.	=	Interpretation strongly implied by the images.
Text is ambiguous and commentators divided.	=	Draw the images to be as ambiguous as the text.

TREATMENT OF THE TEXT

All the words from the translation used. Where the pictorial format makes some words redundant, these are featured in the gutter spaces between the panels. The only "words" added are sound effects.

Minor punctuation (for example speech marks, commas and semi-colons within speech) are rendered redundant where speech bubbles and breaks between panels indicate the pauses or changes in speaker, and have therefore been excluded. An ellipsis has been used where a sentence continues over two or more panels to indicate the continuity of thought. Exclamation marks and question marks have remained in accordance with the translation.

One of the advantages to a pictorial version is the ability to render emotion visually, and in accordance with common use, capitalisation has been used to indicate shouting. Large numbers have been converted to digits to save space and aid readability.

Example: From Judges 14:16. How it appears in the Bible...

"*Samson's wife wept before him, and said, "You just hate me, and don't love me. You've told a riddle to the children of my people, and haven't told it to me." He said to her, "Behold, I haven't told my father or my mother, so why should I tell you?" 17 She wept before him the seven days, while their feast lasted."*

How it appears in the comic...

God shows no favoritism.
In every nation he accepts those who
fear him and do what is right.

Acts 10:34-35

The Word for Word
Bible Comic presents...

The Book of

Ruth

IN THE DAYS WHEN THE JUDGES JUDGED,
THERE WAS A FAMINE IN THE LAND.

A CERTAIN MAN OF BETHLEHEM
JUDAH WENT TO LIVE IN THE
COUNTRY OF MOAB, HE, AND
HIS WIFE, AND HIS TWO SONS.

THE NAME OF THE MAN WAS ELIMELECH

AND THE NAME OF HIS WIFE, NAOMI.

THE NAMES OF HIS TWO SONS WERE MAHLON AND CHILION, EPHRATHITES OF BETHLEHEM JUDAH.

THEY CAME INTO THE COUNTRY OF MOAB...

...AND LIVED THERE.

ELIMELECH, NAOMI'S HUSBAND, DIED

SHE WAS LEFT WITH HER TWO SONS.

THEY TOOK FOR THEMSELVES WIVES OF THE WOMEN OF MOAB.

THE NAME OF THE ONE WAS ORPAH

THE NAME OF THE OTHER WAS RUTH.

THEY LIVED THERE ABOUT TEN YEARS.
MAHLON AND CHILION BOTH DIED, AND THE WOMAN WAS
BEREAVED OF HER TWO CHILDREN AND OF HER HUSBAND.

THEN SHE AROSE WITH HER DAUGHTERS-IN-LAW, THAT SHE MIGHT RETURN FROM THE COUNTRY OF MOAB

FOR SHE HAD HEARD IN THE COUNTRY OF MOAB HOW YAHWEH HAD VISITED HIS PEOPLE IN GIVING THEM BREAD.

SHE WENT OUT OF THE PLACE WHERE SHE WAS, AND HER TWO DAUGHTERS-IN-LAW WITH HER.

THEY WENT ON THE WAY TO RETURN TO THE LAND OF JUDAH.

Go

NAOMI SAID TO HER TWO DAUGHTERS-IN-LAW,

...return each of you to her mother's house.

May Yahweh deal kindly with you, as you have dealt with the dead, and with me.

May Yahweh grant you that you may find rest, each of you in the house of her husband.

THEN SHE KISSED THEM, AND THEY LIFTED UP THEIR VOICES, AND WEPT.

No, but we will return with you to your people.

Go back, my daughters. Why do you want to go with me?

Do I still have sons in my womb, that they may be your husbands? Go back, my daughters, go your way; for I am too old to have a husband.

If I should say, 'I have hope,' if I should even have a husband tonight, and should also bear sons; would you then wait until they were grown?

WOULD YOU THEN REFRAIN FROM HAVING HUSBANDS? NO, MY DAUGHTERS

...for it grieves me seriously for your sakes, for Yahweh's hand has gone out against me.

THEY LIFTED UP THEIR VOICES, AND WEPT AGAIN

THEN ORPAH KISSED HER MOTHER-IN-LAW

BEHOLD, YOUR SISTER-IN-LAW HAS GONE BACK TO HER PEOPLE, AND TO HER GOD. FOLLOW YOUR SISTER-IN-LAW.

Don't urge me to leave you, and to return from following you

FOR

...where you go, I will go; and where you stay, I will stay.

Your people will be my people, and your God my God. Where you die, I will die, and there I will be buried.

May Yahweh do so to me, and more also, if anything but death parts you and me.

WHEN SHE SAW THAT SHE WAS DETERMINED TO GO WITH HER, SHE STOPPED URGING HER.

SO THEY BOTH WENT UNTIL THEY CAME TO BETHLEHEM.

WHEN THEY HAD COME TO BETHLEHEM, ALL THE CITY WAS EXCITED ABOUT THEM

AND THEY ASKED.

SHE SAID TO THEM,

Is this Naomi?

Don't call me Naomi. Call me Mara

for the Almighty has dealt very bitterly with me.

I went out full, and Yahweh has brought me home again empty.

Why do you call me Naomi, since Yahweh has testified against me, and the Almighty has afflicted me?

SO NAOMI RETURNED, AND RUTH THE MOABITESS, HER DAUGHTER-IN-LAW, WITH HER, WHO RETURNED OUT OF THE COUNTRY OF MOAB.

THEY CAME TO BETHLEHEM IN THE BEGINNING OF BARLEY HARVEST.

NAOMI HAD A RELATIVE OF HER HUSBAND'S, A MIGHTY MAN OF WEALTH, OF THE FAMILY OF ELIMELECH, AND HIS NAME WAS BOAZ.

RUTH THE MOABITESS SAID TO NAOMI,

Let me now go to the field, and glean among the ears of grain after him in whose sight I find favor.

SHE SAID TO HER.

Go, my daughter.

SHE WENT, AND CAME AND GLEANED IN THE FIELD AFTER THE REAPERS

SHE HAPPENED TO COME TO THE PORTION OF THE FIELD BELONGING TO BOAZ

WHO WAS OF THE FAMILY OF ELIMELECH.

May Yahweh be with you.

May Yahweh bless you.

THEN BOAZ SAID TO HIS SERVANT WHO WAS SET OVER THE REAPERS,

Whose young lady is this?

It is the Moabite lady who came back with Naomi out of the country of Moab.

She said,

'Please let me glean and gather after the reapers among the sheaves.'

So she came, and has continued even from the morning until now, except that she rested a little in the house.

THE SERVANT WHO WAS SET OVER THE REAPERS ANSWERED,

THEN BOAZ SAID TO RUTH,

Listen, my daughter.

Don't go to glean in another field, and don't go from here, but stay here close to my maidens.

Let your eyes be on the field that they reap, and go after them.

Haven't I commanded the young men not to touch you?

When you are thirsty, go to the vessels, and drink from that which the young men have drawn.

AND SAID TO HIM,

Why have I found favor in your sight, that you should take knowledge of me, since I am a foreigner?

THEN SHE FELL ON HER FACE, AND BOWED HERSELF TO THE GROUND.

BOAZ ANSWERED HER,

I have been fully told about all that you have done to your mother-in-law since the death of your husband, and how you have left your father and your mother, and the land of your birth, and have come to a people that you didn't know before.

May Yahweh repay your work, and a full reward be given to you from Yahweh, the God of Israel, under whose wings you have come to take refuge.

THEN SHE SAID,

Let me find favor in your sight, my lord, because you have comforted me...

...and because you have spoken kindly to your servant, though I am not as one of your servants.

AT MEAL TIME

COME HERE, AND EAT SOME BREAD, AND DIP YOUR MORSEL IN THE VINEGAR.

SHE SAT BESIDE THE REAPERS, AND THEY PASSED HER PARCHED GRAIN,

AND SHE ATE, AND WAS SATISFIED, AND LEFT SOME OF IT.

WHEN SHE HAD RISEN UP TO GLEAN, BOAZ COMMANDED HIS YOUNG MEN, SAYING,

Let her glean even among the sheaves, and don't reproach her.

Also pull out some for her from the bundles, and leave it. Let her glean, and don't rebuke her.

SO SHE GLEANED IN THE FIELD UNTIL EVENING

AND
SHE BEAT OUT THAT WHICH SHE HAD GLEANED, AND IT WAS ABOUT AN EPHAH OF BARLEY.

SHE TOOK IT UP, AND WENT INTO THE CITY.

THEN HER MOTHER-IN-LAW SAW WHAT SHE HAD GLEANED; AND SHE BROUGHT OUT AND GAVE TO HER THAT WHICH SHE HAD LEFT AFTER SHE HAD ENOUGH.

HER MOTHER-IN-LAW SAID TO HER,

Where have you gleaned today? Where have you worked? Blessed be he who noticed you.

SHE TOLD HER MOTHER-IN-LAW WITH WHOM SHE HAD WORKED...

The man's name with whom I worked today is Boaz.

NAOMI SAID TO HER DAUGHTER-IN-LAW,

May he be blessed by Yahweh...

...who has not left off his kindness to the living and to the dead.

NAOMI SAID TO HER,

The man is a close relative to us, one of our near kinsmen.

RUTH THE MOABITESS SAID,

Yes, he said to me, 'You shall stay close to my young men, until they have finished all my harvest.'

NAOMI SAID TO RUTH HER DAUGHTER-IN-LAW

It is good, my daughter, that you go out with his maidens, and that they not meet you in any other field.

SO SHE STAYED CLOSE TO THE MAIDENS OF BOAZ, TO GLEAN TO THE END OF BARLEY HARVEST AND OF WHEAT HARVEST

AND SHE LIVED WITH HER MOTHER-IN-LAW.

NAOMI HER MOTHER-IN-LAW SAID TO HER,

My daughter, shall I not seek rest for you, that it may be well with you?

Now isn't Boaz our kinsman, with whose maidens you were?

Therefore wash yourself, anoint yourself, get dressed, and go down to the threshing floor...

"...but don't make yourself known to the man until he has finished eating and drinking."

WHEN BOAZ HAD EATEN AND DRUNK, AND HIS HEART WAS MERRY, HE WENT TO LIE DOWN AT THE END OF THE HEAP OF GRAIN.

SHE SAID TO HER

"It shall be, when he lies down, that you shall note the place where he is lying. Then you shall go in, uncover his feet, and lay down. Then he will tell you what to do."

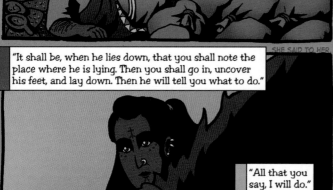

"All that you say, I will do."

SHE WENT DOWN TO THE THRESHING FLOOR, AND DID EVERYTHING THAT HER MOTHER-IN-LAW TOLD HER.

SHE CAME SOFTLY...

AT MIDNIGHT...

UNCOVERED HIS FEET, AND LAID DOWN.

THE MAN WAS STARTLED AND TURNED HIMSELF; AND BEHOLD, A WOMAN LAY AT HIS FEET, HE SAID.

WHO ARE YOU?

I am Ruth your servant.

Therefore spread the corner of your garment over your servant; for you are a near kinsman.

You are blessed by Yahweh, my daughter.

You have shown more kindness in the latter end than at the beginning, because you didn't follow young men, whether poor or rich.

Now, my daughter, don't be afraid. I will do to you all that you say; for all the city of my people knows that you are a worthy woman.

Now it is true that I am a near kinsman. However, there is a kinsman nearer than I.

Stay this night, and in the morning, if he will perform for you the part of a kinsman...

...good.

Let him do the kinsman's duty.

But if he will not do the duty of a kinsman for you, then I will do the duty of a kinsman for you, as Yahweh lives.

Lie down until the morning.

SHE LAY AT HIS FEET UNTIL THE MORNING

THEN SHE ROSE UP BEFORE ONE COULD DISCERN ANOTHER.

FOR HE SAID,

Let it not be known that the woman came to the threshing floor.

HE SAID,

Bring the mantle that is on you, and hold it.

SHE HELD IT; AND HE MEASURED SIX MEASURES OF BARLEY, AND LAID IT ON HER

THEN HE WENT INTO THE CITY.

WHEN SHE CAME TO HER MOTHER-IN-LAW, SHE SAID,

How did it go, my daughter?

SHE TOLD HER ALL THAT THE MAN HAD DONE FOR HER.

SHE SAID,

He gave me these six measures of barley; for he said, 'Don't go empty to your mother-in-law.'

THEN SHE SAID,

Wait, my daughter, until you know what will happen; for the man will not rest until he has settled this today.

THEN BOAZ SAID,

NOW THIS WAS THE CUSTOM IN FORMER TIME IN ISRAEL CONCERNING REDEEMING AND CONCERNING EXCHANGING, TO CONFIRM ALL THINGS: A MAN TOOK OFF HIS SHOE, AND GAVE IT TO HIS NEIGHBOR; AND THIS WAS THE WAY OF LEGALIZING TRANSACTIONS IN ISRAEL.

SO THE NEAR KINSMAN SAID TO BOAZ,

BOAZ SAID TO THE ELDERS, AND TO ALL THE PEOPLE,

THEN HE TOOK OFF HIS SHOE.

WE ARE WITNESSES.

May Yahweh make the woman who has come into your house like Rachel and like Leah, which both built the house of Israel

...and treat you worthily in Ephrathah, and be famous in Bethlehem.

Let your house be like the house of Perez, whom Tamar bore to Judah, of the offspring which Yahweh will give you by this young woman.

SO BOAZ TOOK RUTH, AND SHE BECAME HIS WIFE

YAHWEH ENABLED HER TO CONCEIVE, AND SHE BORE A SON.

THE WOMEN SAID TO NAOMI,

Blessed be Yahweh, who has not left you today without a near kinsman.

Let his name be famous in Israel.

He shall be to you a restorer of life, and sustain you in your old age, for your daughter-in-law, who loves you, who is better to you than seven sons, has given birth to him.

NAOMI TOOK THE CHILD, AND LAID HIM IN HER BOSOM, AND BECAME NURSE TO IT. THE WOMEN, HER NEIGHBORS, GAVE HIM A NAME, SAYING,

A son is born to Naomi.

THEY NAMED HIM OBED. HE IS THE FATHER OF JESSE, THE FATHER OF DAVID.

Relevant passages from other books of the Bible

LAW OF THE LEVIRATE MARRIAGE

Deuteronomy 25:5-10 World English Bible (WEB)

If brothers dwell together, and one of them dies, and has no son, the wife of the dead shall not be married outside to a stranger. Her husband's brother shall go in to her, and take her as his wife, and perform the duty of a husband's brother to her. It shall be that the firstborn whom she bears shall succeed in the name of his brother who is dead, that his name not be blotted out of Israel.

If the man doesn't want to take his brother's wife, then his brother's wife shall go up to the gate to the elders, and say, "My husband's brother refuses to raise up to his brother a name in Israel. He will not perform the duty of a husband's brother to me." Then the elders of his city shall call him, and speak to him: and if he stands and says, "I don't want to take her"; then his brother's wife shall come to him in the presence of the elders, and loose his shoe from off his foot, and spit in his face. She shall answer and say, "So shall it be done to the man who does not build up his brother's house." His name shall be called in Israel, "The house of him who had his shoe removed."

LAW OF GLEANING

Leviticus 23:22 World English Bible (WEB)

"'When you reap the harvest of your land, you must not wholly reap into the corners of your field, and you must not gather the gleanings of your harvest. You must leave them for the poor, and for the foreigner. I am Yahweh your God.'"

CONTINUED GENEALOGY NAMING BOAZ'S MOTHER

Matthew 1:1-16 World English Bible (WEB)

The book of the genealogy of Jesus Christ, the son of David, the son of Abraham. Abraham became the father of Isaac. Isaac became the father of Jacob. Jacob became the father of Judah and his brothers. Judah became the father of Perez and Zerah by Tamar. Perez became the father of Hezron. Hezron became the father of Ram. Ram became the father of Amminadab. Amminadab became the father of Nahshon. Nahshon became the father of Salmon. Salmon became the father of Boaz by Rahab. Boaz became the father of Obed by Ruth. Obed became the father of Jesse. Jesse became the father of King David. David became the father of Solomon by her who had been Uriah's wife. Solomon became the father of Rehoboam. Rehoboam became the father of Abijah. Abijah became the father of Asa. Asa became the father of Jehoshaphat. Jehoshaphat became the father of Joram. Joram became the father of Uzziah. Uzziah became the father of Jotham. Jotham became the father of Ahaz. Ahaz became the father of Hezekiah. Hezekiah became the father of Manasseh. Manasseh became the father of Amon. Amon became the father of Josiah. Josiah became the father of Jechoniah and his brothers, at the time of the exile to Babylon. After the exile to Babylon, Jechoniah became the father of Shealtiel. Shealtiel became the father of Zerubbabel. Zerubbabel became the father of Abiud. Abiud became the father of Eliakim. Eliakim became the father of Azor. Azor became the father of Zadok. Zadok became the father of Achim. Achim became the father of Eliud. Eliud became the father of Eleazar. Eleazar became the father of Matthan. Matthan became the father of Jacob. Jacob became the father of Joseph, the husband of Mary, from whom was born Jesus, who is called Christ.

The Promised Land

The time of the Judges

SIDON

DAMASCUS

MT LEBANON

MT HERMON

Pharpar

AHLAB

Leontes

TYRE

LAISH
(DAN)

DAN

MT MEROM   KEDESH

SHOB

HAZOR

ASHER   **NAPHTALI**

ACCO

CAPERNAUM

APHEK

CABUL

GOLAN   Ashtaroth

RIMMON

KEDRON

ZEBULUN

HAROSETH-
HAGGOYIM

NAZARETH

NAHALAL   MT TABOR   EN-HADDAH

Yarmuk

EDREI

DOR

MT GILBOA   **ISSACHAR**   MT MOREH

KAMON

MANASSEH

MEGIDDO   OPHRAH

JEZREEL

BETH SHITTAR

Shihor-Libnath   TAANACH   GILBOA   BETH-SHEAN

RAMOTH-GILEAD

EN-GANNIM

JABESH-GILEAD

ISLEAM

DOTHAN

Jordan   Jabbok

SOCOR   **MANASSEH**   BEZEK   ABEL MEHOLAH

THEBEZ   ZAPHON   GERASA

SHAMIR

MT EBAL   SUCCOTH   MAHANAIM

Kanah   SHECHEM   PENIEL

PIRATHON   MT GERIZIM   **GILEAD**

APHEK   ZARETHAN   MIZPAH

EPHRAIM   LEBONAH   TAPPUAH   ADAM   MT GILEAD

JOPPA   SHILOH

Aijalon   MT GAASH   JOGBEHAH

LOD   TIMNATH-SERAH   **GAD**

OPHRAH   JAZER   RABBAH

BEZEK

JABNEH   GEZER   MIZPAH   BETHEL

MT HERES   AI

AIJALON   **BENJAMIN**   GILGAL   JERICHO

GIBEAH

ASHDOD   TIMNAH   MT JEARIM   HESHBON   BEZER

EKRON   JEBUS   BETH HOGLAH

GATH   BETH SHEMESH   (JERUSALEM)   MT NEBO   MINNITH

DAN   BETHLEHEM   MEDEBA

ACHZIB

MARESHAH   BETH-ZUR   **REUBEN**

ASHKELON

LACHISH

GAZA   HEBRON

ENGEDI   DIBON

GERAR   **JUDAH**   AROER

ZIGLAG   DEBIR   Arnon

ESHTEMOA

SIMEON   ARAD   KIR-HARESETH

SHARUHEN   BEERSHEBA

HORMAH

NEGEV

Zered Brook

BEER

0 Miles   10   20   30

TAMAR

THE ASCENT
OF AKRABBIM   BOZRAH

DESIGNING RUTH

When designing Ruth I wanted her to look exotic and interesting, and I wanted to contrast her appearance with that of the Israelite women. Therefore her head is uncovered, her hair is styled, and she has makeup. She also has piercings and tattoos. In Leviticus 19:28 the Lord commands the Israelites not to have tattoos or cut themselves (including ritual scarring); the context implies that this is the common practice of the other nations around them.

The lifestyle and heritage linked to Moab and Israel (and a few other biblical people groups) is that of Bedouin culture. Even today, tattoos are commonplace among various Bedouin tribes for both men and women. Ruth's tattoos are based on these. Although they are prominent on her face they are actually quite restrained examples of this practice. They were also useful aspects to exaggerate when the "near kinsman" imagines how a Moabite woman would look.

In her natural habitat Ruth has Moabite clothes, which have much in common with Egyptian styles of the day. One of the best examples is on the Stela of Balua. However, when she goes to Bethlehem, she tries to fit in by covering her head and wearing her late husband's Simla (cloak).

DESIGNING NAOMI

I designed Naomi to be a typical Judahite woman, with the nose shape I draw as a hallmark of the clans descended from Leah. She has a necklace with three lion's claw motifs, but these are silver rather than real claws, as lions are ritually impure for faithful Israelites. She has borne two children who are grown to maturity, so she is probably in her forties in the first part of the story, and then her fifties in the later part.

DESIGNING BOAZ

This image was the master for drawing her. I have tried to use diverse and reI discovered some interesting things about Boaz as I researched him. Those who know the character will know that his name means "strength", so I wanted to draw him as a strapping fellow. It became apparent, studying the genealogies and considering his remarks in Ruth 3:10 - and the fact he defaults to calling Ruth "My daughter" (תַב) - that he is much older than Ruth. In Jewish tradition (in the Midrash Zutta) it is conjectured that Boaz was as old as eighty. I've drawn him a little younger than that, but with Biblical large ages we can't be sure what an eighty-year-old would look like - Caleb, who is eighty-five, claims to be as fit as when he was forty (Joshua 14:11).

Ethnically, Boaz is the son of Salmon, a prince of the clan of Judah, but in Matthew 6:5 we learn that his mother was Rahab the "harlot" from Joshua 2. We know that she was a Canaanite, so Boaz must be half Canaanite, which might explain his charity towards non-Israelite outsiders... but this additionally means that his son Obed was half Moabite, a quarter Canaanite and a quarter Judahite genetically. Legal status comes through the father, of course, so they are both legally fully Israelite, but I found Obed's genetic background very interesting, particularly as the royal line is the upshot of these unions.

He wears the same cloak his father Salmon wore, as you will see in the upcoming Joshua Word for Word Bible Comic. The gold lion cloak-pin/brooch will be worn throughout many generations in the comic. It originates with Nahshon from the gold gathered in the Exodus, and we can see David wearing it in the final panel of this book.

MOABITES

There are extremely limited sources on the appearance of Moabite, but luckily there is one good source call the Balua Stela in the American Museum, which depicts what seems to be a Moabite ruler with the male deity Baal and a female who may be a goddess or the queen. From this stela, we can see they wear clothes very similar to contemporary Egyptian styles. One of the only other Moabite depictions is on the Warrior God stela in the Louve. The god or warrior has an interesting top knot, long curling ponytail and patterns on his kilt.

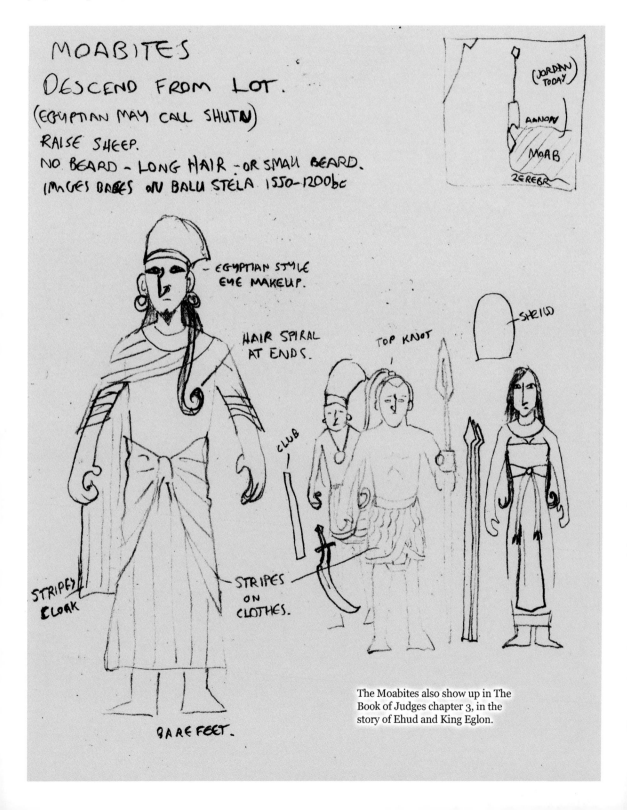

MOABITES
DESCEND FROM LOT.
(EGYPTIAN MAY CALL SHUTN)
RAISE SHEEP.
NO BEARD - LONG HAIR - OR SMALL BEARD.
IMAGES BASED ON BALU STELA 1550-1200bc

(JORDAN TODAY)

ARNON

MOAB

ZEREBR

- EGYPTIAN STYLE EYE MAKEUP.

HAIR SPIRAL AT ENDS.

TOP KNOT

SHEILD

CLUB

STRIPED CLOAK

STRIPES ON CLOTHES.

BARE FEET.

The Moabites also show up in The Book of Judges chapter 3, in the story of Ehud and King Eglon.

ISRAELITE GARB

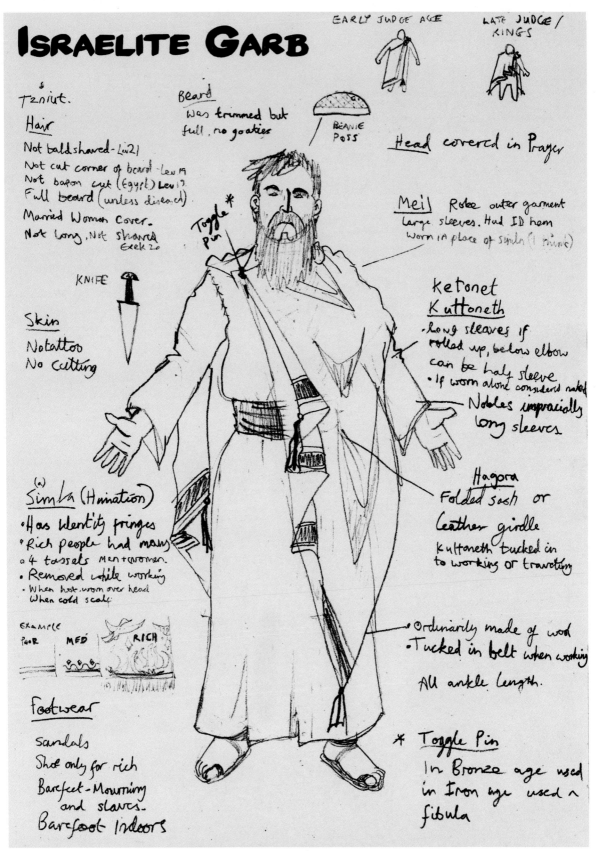

EARLY JUDGE AGE

LATE JUDGE / KINGS

Tzniut.

Hair
Not bald shaved - Lev 21
Not cut corner of beard - Lev 19
Not bazon cut (Egypt) Lev 19
Full beard (unless diseased)
Married Woman Cover.
Not Long, Not shaved
Ezek 20

Beard
Was trimmed but full, no goaties

BEANIE POSS

Head covered in Prayer

KNIFE

Skin
No tattoo
No cutting

Toggle Pin *

Meil Robe outer garment
Large sleeves. Had ID hem
worn in place of simla (I think)

ketonet Kuttoneth
- Long sleeves if rolled up, below elbow can be half sleeve
- If worn alone considered naked
- Nobles impracially long sleeves

(a) Simla (Himation)
- Has identity fringes
- Rich people had many
- 4 tassels Men + women.
- Removed while working
- When hot worn over head
  When cold scalf

EXAMPLE POOR   MED   RICH

Hagora
Folded sash or Leather girdle
kuttoneth tucked in to working or travelling

- Ordinarily made of wool
- Tucked in belt when working
  All ankle length.

Footwear
Sandals
Shoe only for rich
Barefeet - Mourning and slaves.
Barefoot Indoors

* **Toggle Pin**
In Bronze age used
in Iron age used a fibula

This is a rough sheet on which I kept my notes on Israelite dress. At the top right the tiny men show the two main ways that I have the Hebrews wearing their Simla/cloaks. As the Judges period spans 300 years I used this to show a change from the start of the period to the end. It's also helpful to give clues that the events in the last 5 chapters of the book actually happen at the start of the time period, between the death of Joshua and the oppression of Cushan-Rishathaim. The early style is based on the way Semitic people are depicted wearing their cloaks in Egyptian images.

CANAANITES

The term Amorite and Canaanite seems to be interchangeable. We know from Genesis 10 that Canaan is the ancestor of the Amorites, as well as other tribes, but in the text it seems likely is that Canaanite is labeling the people by where they live and Amorite is a name for the people group. They are also descended from Ham (the son of Noah) who is the father of most of the African nations, unlike Israel who are Semitic because they are descended from Shem. Amorites are said to be tall in Amos 2:9 and Sihon and Og are both Amorite Rephaites (Giants).

Their colour scheme is purples, lilacs, maroons and similar colours as they are known as the "Purple People" as dye from the murex is a very significant industry in Canaan. As in the murals of ancient Egypt, they also have a lot of patterns on their clothes.

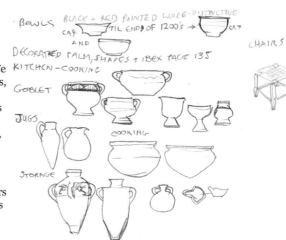

BOWLS   BLACK + RED PAINTED WARE - DISTINCTIVE
CA4   (TIL ENDS OF 1200'S →) CA4
AND
DECORATED PALM, SHAPES + IBEX PAGE 135
KITCHEN - COOKING
GOBLET
JUGS
COOKING
STORAGE
CHAIRS

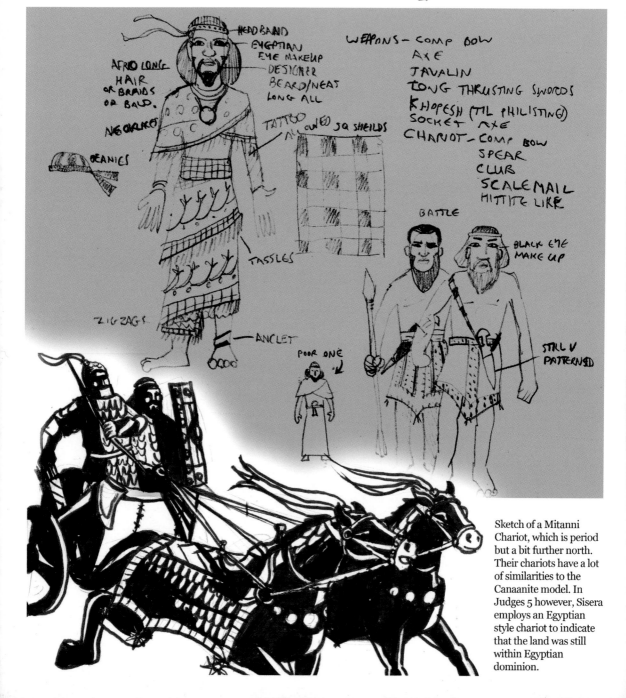

HEAD BAND
EGYPTIAN EYE MAKEUP
DESIGNER
BEARD/NEAT
LONG ALL
AFRO LONG HAIR OR BRAIDS OR BALD.
NECKLACE
BEANIES
TATTOO ALLOWED SQ SHEILDS
TASSLES
ZIGZAGS
ANCLET
POOR ONE

WEAPONS - COMP BOW
AXE
JAVALIN
LONG THRUSTING SWORDS
KHOPESH (TIL PHILISTING)
SOCKET AXE
CHARIOT - COMP BOW
SPEAR
CLUB
SCALE MAIL
HITTITE LIKE

BATTLE
BLACK EYE MAKE UP
STILL V PATTERNED

Sketch of a Mitanni Chariot, which is period but a bit further north. Their chariots have a lot of similarities to the Canaanite model. In Judges 5 however, Sisera employs an Egyptian style chariot to indicate that the land was still within Egyptian dominion.

Alternate cover design for the Book of Ruth, in rough.

THE BOOK OF RUTH

SIMON AMADEUS PILLARIO

THE NEXT SIX PAGES GIVE A PREVIEW
FROM THE BOOK OF JOSHUA,
COMING SOON.

IT INCLUDES WHEN BOAZ'S PARENTS,
RAHAB AND SALMON, MEET.

JOSHUA CHAPTER 2: 1-24

WORD BIBLE COMIC

THEY WENT AND CAME INTO THE HOUSE OF A PROSTITUTE WHOSE NAME WAS RAHAB

AND SLEPT THERE.

THE KING OF JERICHO

WAS TOLD,

JERICHO'S KING SENT

Behold, men of the children of Israel came in here tonight to spy out the land.

TO RAHAB

BAM BAM BAM

SAYING

Bring out the men who have come to you, who have entered into your house

for they have come to spy out all the land.

THE WOMAN TOOK THE TWO MEN AND HID THEM, THEN SHE SAID

Yes, the men came to me, but I didn't know where they came from. About the time of the shutting of the gate, when it was dark, the men went out. Where the men went, I don't know.

Pursue them quickly. You may catch up with them.

BUT SHE HAD BROUGHT THEM UP TO THE ROOF, AND HIDDEN THEM UNDER THE STALKS OF FLAX WHICH SHE HAD LAID IN ORDER ON THE ROOF.

THE MEN PURSUED THEM ALONG THE WAY TO THE FORDS OF THE JORDAN RIVER. AS SOON AS THOSE WHO PURSUED THEM HAD GONE OUT, THEY SHUT THE GATE.

BEFORE THEY HAD LAIN DOWN, SHE CAME UP TO THEM ON THE ROOF.

I know that Yahweh has given you the land

...and that the fear of you has fallen upon us, and that all the inhabitants of the land melt away before you.

For we have heard how Yahweh dried up the water of the Red Sea before you, when you came out of Egypt...

...and what you did to the two kings of the Amorites, who were beyond the Jordan, to Sihon and to Og, whom you utterly destroyed.

As soon as we had heard it, our hearts melted, and there wasn't any more spirit in any man, because of you...

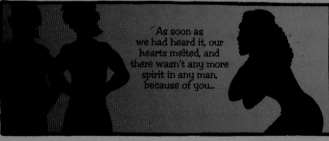

Now therefore, please swear to me by Yahweh, since I have dealt kindly with you, that you also will deal kindly with my father's house, and give me a true sign;

and that you will save alive my father, my mother, my brothers, and my sisters, and all that they have, and will deliver our lives from death.

...for Yahweh your God, he is God in heaven above, and on earth beneath.

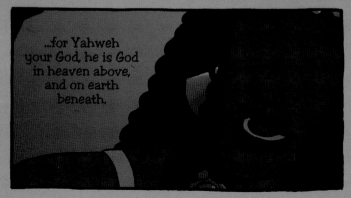

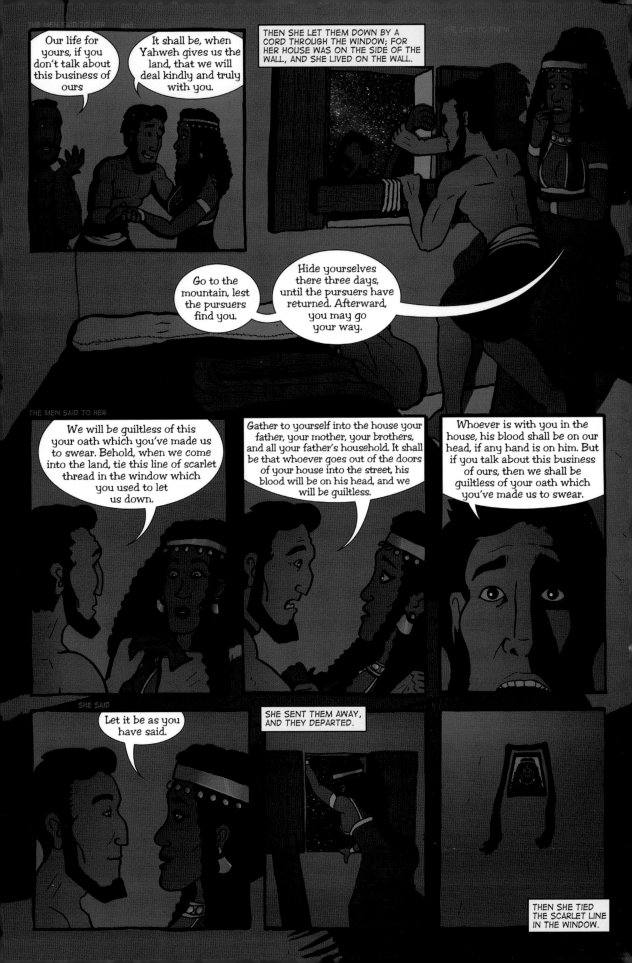